U.S. Tank Destroyers
in action

By Jim Mesko
Color by Don Greer
Illustrated by Ernesto Cumpian
and David Smith

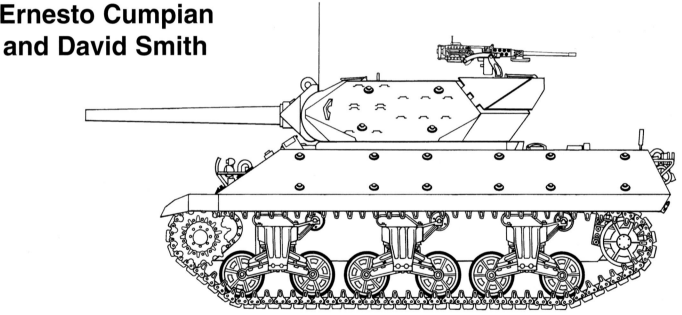

Armor Number 36

squadron/signal publications

An M18 Hellcat of the 824th Tank Destroyer Battalion, fires on German positions in Wiesloch, Germany during April of 1945 in support of the 2nd Battalion, 397th Infantry Regiment, 100th Division, VI Corps, 7th Army.

Acknowledgements:

Canadian Archives
US Army (USA)
US Marine Corps (USMC)
Patton Armor Museum (PAM)
National Archives (NA)
Mike Green
Dave Spenser
Richard Cole
George Balin
Richard Hunnicutt
Ed Storey

Dedication:

To the staffs of the Patton Armor Museum and the National Archives without whose help this book would not have been possible.

ISBN 0-89747-385-X

If you have any photographs of aircraft, armor, soldiers or ships of any nation, particularly wartime snapshots, why not share them with us and help make Squadron/Signal's books all the more interesting and complete in the future. Any photograph sent to us will be copied and the original returned. The donor will be fully credited for any photos used. Please send them to:

Squadron/Signal Publications, Inc.
1115 Crowley Drive
Carrollton, TX 75011-5010

Если у вас есть фотографии самолётов, вооружения, солдат или кораблей любой страны, особенно, снимки времён войны, поделитесь с нами и помогите сделать новые книги издательства Эскадрон/Сигнал ещё интереснее. Мы переснимем ваши фотографии и вернём оригиналы. Имена приславших снимки будут сопровождать все опубликованные фотографии. Пожалуйста, присылайте фотографии по адресу:

Squadron/Signal Publications, Inc.
1115 Crowley Drive
Carrollton, TX 75011-5010

軍用機、装甲車両、兵士、軍艦などの写真を所持しておられる方はいらっしゃいませんか？どの国のものでも結構です。作戦中に撮影されたものが特に良いのです。Squadron/Signal社の出版する刊行物において、このような写真は内容を一層充実し、興味深くすることができます。当方にお送り頂いた写真は、複写の後お返しいたします。出版物中に写真を使用した場合は、必ず提供者のお名前を明記させて頂きます。お写真は下記にご送付ください。

Squadron/Signal Publications, Inc.
1115 Crowley Drive
Carrollton, TX 75011-5010

An M10 of the 703rd Tank Destroyer Battalion, 3rd Armored Division, advances past a knocked out Panzer IV near Langlir, Belgium in the waning days of the Battle of the Bulge. The .50 caliber machine gun is mounted on the forward edge of the turret to improve its field of fire. The vehicle also lacks any kind of white camouflage to help it blend into its surroundings. While the 3 inch gun of the M10 could handle older German tanks such as the Pzkfw IV, the newer Panthers and Tigers proved much more difficult to defeat, especially head-on at extended ranges. The crew has stowed a great deal of personal gear on the outside of the turret due to the limited amount of room on the inside of the M10. (USA/NA)

Introduction

When tanks were first used by the British and French in World War One, they caught the Germans totally by surprise. Had this surprise been exploited, the course of the war might have been different. Unfortunately, the initial employment ended in failure, and in the interim the Germans developed tactics to counter this new battlefield weapon. Lacking tanks of their own the Germans resorted to artillery to counter tanks, either by massive artillery bombardments or by moving artillery to the point of the attack. This mobile employment of artillery, particularly the 77mm cannon, was the first use of weapons in the anti-tank or tank destroyer role, even though they had not been designed for this role. As the war progressed, tactics used to counter tank attacks were modified and improved, but no new weapons had been developed for the anti-tank role.

Following the war, most emphasis was placed on small, lightweight towed weapons which were considered sufficient given the state of tanks and tactics of the time. Although some thought was given to innovative doctrine in both Great Britain and the Soviet Union, by and large little progress was made in revising tactics which remained much as they had in World War One. When civil war broke out in Spain in 1936 tanks were used by both sides, but with little overall effect on the battlefield. Poor tactical employment led to high losses on both sides, which tended to reinforce the low opinion which many armies had for the employment of tanks. This all changed dramatically in September 1939, when Germany invaded Poland. The German Army, under the guidance of General Heinz Guderian, had developed new tank tactics based on mass, maneuver, and air support. Called *Blitzkrieg* (Lightning War) this new style of warfare overwhelmed Poland in a month, far faster than military experts had anticipated. However many military experts insisted this was attributed more to the lack of Polish military ability than to German prowess.

If some thought the Polish campaign was a fluke, the following spring the Germans smashed Belgium, Holland, and France in six weeks and drove the remnants of the British Army off the continent from Dunkirk. In the United States this overwhelming German victory was attributed to the fact that Germany had employed huge numbers of superior tanks in their *Blitzkrieg* attack. In reality this was far from the truth, the Allies actually had more tanks, and most were superior to the majority of German armor. However, the revolutionary tactics of the *panzer* divisions striking "en mass" was the real reason for their success, though the Germans did indeed foster the illusion of superior tanks and numbers in their propaganda. This, coupled with poor tactics and poor deployment of the Allied armor, was what really led to such a one-sided victory for the Germans.

American military officials were just as stunned by this German victory as were their British and French counterparts. US army officers realized the United States had no tank worthy of the name. The few tanks available were lightly armored and carried either a light cannon or machine guns. None were a match for the German tanks and there were no designs in the works which would be able to quickly redress the situation. While some progress had been made in reorganizing and restructuring the armored forces, the German victory led officials to look at the creation of a specific type of unit to deal directly with enemy tanks. This was officially laid out in May of 1941 when a directive was issued for the establishment of a mobile force armed with heavy weapons to deal directly with the threat of enemy armor. While there were varying views on how to do this, it came down to using either tanks or anti-tank guns. To test the concept a number of experimental anti-tank units were formed to take part in the 1941 War Games in North Carolina. The results were favorable for the use of anti-tank weapons, and led to the forming of specific anti-tank battalions which were to be split between divisions

The first serious attempt by the US Army to mount an anti-tank weapon for use against enemy armor occurred in 1937 when a 47mm cannon was mounted in a small, soft steel, opened top turret on an M2A1 light tank. Though designed for use against hidden anti-tank guns it was also tested against moving targets to see if it could be used in the anti-tank role. The tests were not successful, however, and the project was dropped. (Hunnicutt)

With the fall of France by what appeared to be swarms of German tanks, Army officials looked for ways to give its gunners more mobility. There were a number of attempts to mount the Army's standard 37mm anti-tank gun on the chassis of the new jeep, but limited room on the jeep for the crew and ammunition made such a idea impractical, even though the jeep could carry the gun. In addition some officials felt that a much larger gun would be needed to handle the newer German tanks which were being developed. (PAM)

and a central command.

When the first units of the new "tank destroyer" formation were authorized just prior to the attack on Pearl Harbor, they were not placed under divisional command but formed as separate units under General Headquarters control. At the same time, the Tank Destroyer Center, was formed at Ft. Meade, Maryland on 1 December 1941. This new organization had the enthusiastic support of Lieutenant General Lesley McNair, the head of Army Ground Forces. General McNair favored the use of anti-tank guns to fight enemy armor rather than other tanks. Under his influence the new Tank Destroyer force developed an aggressive, offensive posture relying on heavily armed and highly mobile vehicles.

Unfortunately, no such vehicle was on hand to fulfill this requirement. Following World War One there had been some effort to mobilize artillery, but with little success. Some thought was given to using such self-propelled artillery in the anti-tank role, but again little was done to implement this line of thought. In October of 1936, a 47mm cannon, basically an enlarged version of the 37mm gun currently in use by the Army, was mounted in a soft steel turret fitted to an M2A1 light tank hull. While designed specifically for use against concealed anti-tank guns, tests were also conducted for its use in the anti-tank role. However, the poor performance of the modified gun resulted in unsatisfactory test results, and further work on the project was canceled.

By early 1940 the Army began to look for ways to make their existing anti-tank guns more mobile. At that time the standard anti-tank weapon was the 37mm cannon, a relatively lightweight weapon which was quite small. Due to these characteristics attempts were made to mount the gun on a jeep chassis. While this proved technically possible, the small size of the jeep made it impractical since little ammunition could be carried, and there was not enough room for a gun crew. Other vehicles were also fitted with the cannon, including the new T22

Gun Motor Carriage and the 3/4 ton weapons carrier which would receive the test designation T21. In the US Army system, prototype and test vehicles were given a 'T' designation. Vehicles later approved for production were assigned an 'M' designation.

Although the 37mm gun was similar in performance to anti-tank weapons in use by other countries, Army officials realized heavier weapons would soon be needed to deal with newer tanks being developed in Germany. With an eye toward mobility, the Army Ordnance department decided to mount a 3 inch gun on a Cleveland Tractor Company high speed tractor, which were used for towing aircraft. Under the designation T1, a modified T9 3 inch gun was mounted at the rear of the chassis. Development began in late 1940, and in January of 1942 the vehicle was reclassified as the M5 3 inch Gun Motor Carriage. An order for 1580 M5s was placed, but continual problems with the vehicle delayed production. By the time problems with the M5 were finally worked out, it had been superseded by the M3 75mm and the M10 Gun Motor Carriages which were ready for production. The M5 project was canceled.

Another effort to create a viable tank destroyer was somewhat more successful. By 1941 the new M3 Halftrack was just coming into service. During the summer of 1941, an M1897A3 75mm cannon, based on the famous French 75mm cannon of World War One, was mounted on an M3 Halftrack just behind the middle of the driver's compartment. The gun mount was welded atop a box on the M3's floor, which also had a rack for nineteen rounds of ammunition. Floor bins held an additional forty rounds. In order to provide room for the gun to pivot and the gun crew to work, the fuel tanks were moved from immediately behind the driver's compartment to the rear of the fighting compartment. A small, flat shield for the gun crew's protection was fitted on the gun. This new vehicle received the designation T12, and was subjected to field tests. By October of 1941 these tests were successfully completed and the vehicle was accepted for production under the designation M3 75mm Gun Motor Carriage (GMC).

The Army Ordnance Department mounted a 3 inch gun on the rear of a Cleveland Tractor Company high speed tractor. While the tractor did provide the necessary mobility for a large weapon, numerous problems arose with the design. There was relatively little armored protection, the weight was much higher than originally specified, and the number of rounds the vehicle could carry was 25% below what was required. Since newer vehicles with better overall performance were coming into service the project was terminated in the summer of 1942. (Hunnicutt)

The T12 which was an M3 Halftrack fitted with an M1897M3 75mm cannon which was mounted in the rear compartment of the M3. This simple conversion worked out amazingly well from a technical point of view and, after field testing, the T12 was standardized as the M3 75mm Gun Motor Carriage (GMC). This became the Army's first tank destroyer. Initial vehicles were fitted with a flat shield on the gun but field reports coming back from the Philippines indicated the need for more protection. As a result a larger, box-like gun shield was developed which provided much more protection. (USA/NA)

DEVELOPMENT

M3 75mm GMC

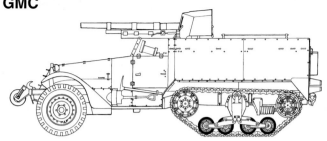

M6 37mm GMC

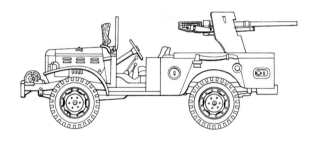

M10 GMC (Early)

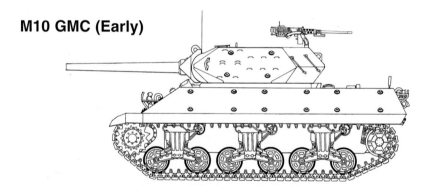

M10 GMC (Mid-Prod)

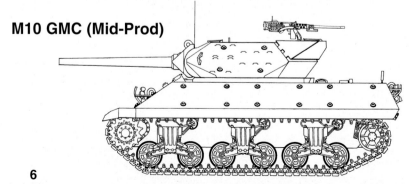

Achilles IIc

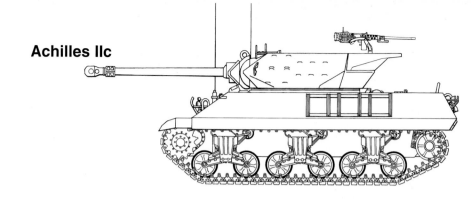

M36 GMC

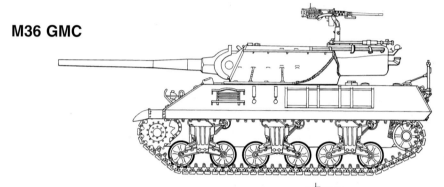

M36B1 GMC

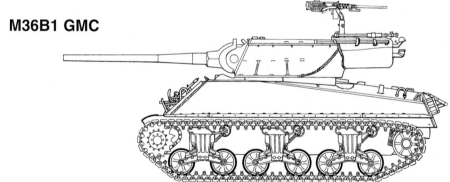

M18 Hellcat

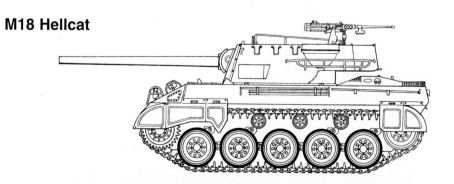

M3 75mm Gun Motor Carriage

The M3 75mm GMC was accepted for production in October 1941, as the main tank destroyer for the rapidly expanding US Army ground forces. The 75mm cannon had a limited traverse of 19 degrees to the left and 21 degrees to the right. It could be elevated from -10 degrees through +29 degrees. In the anti-tank role it had a maximum effective range of 1,000 yards when using armor piercing rounds. The ability to fire high explosive (HE) and smoke rounds also made it useful in support of both armored and infantry units when not employed in the anti-tank role.

The initial vehicles had only a small, flat shield for the protection of the crew. This was considered sufficient until combat reports from the Philippines, where many of the T12's and early production vehicles had been sent to bolster the American garrison, indicated a need for better crew protection. A number of different types of shields arrangements were tried until an angular box type shield was settled on. This was accepted for production during the spring of 1942 and remained unchanged until production ended in April of 1943.

While the M3 75mm GMC was a stopgap measure, it turned out to be one of the more successful types which was rushed into production during the early days of the war. One problem arose during production when stocks of newer 75mm gun mounts were depleted. In their place an older 75mm mount was substituted. These vehicles received the designation M3A1 75mm GMC and aside from the differences in the gun mount the two vehicles were identical.

When production began in late 1941 it was with the idea that the M3 75mm GMC would only be a limited production model until new designs were ready for service. However, it remained in production until nearly the middle of 1943 when production ceased after 2,202 had been completed. Later, when the new fully tracked M10 and M18 tank destroyers were introduced into service, many of these vehicles would be converted back to their basic half-track configuration

Based in part on combat reports from the Philippines. the original flat shield was found to provide very little protection for the gun crew and a new one was developed. This new design was box-like in shape and gave much better protection than the early type. The armored windshield folded downward on this M3. On the standard halftrack it was hinged to fold upward. (PAM)

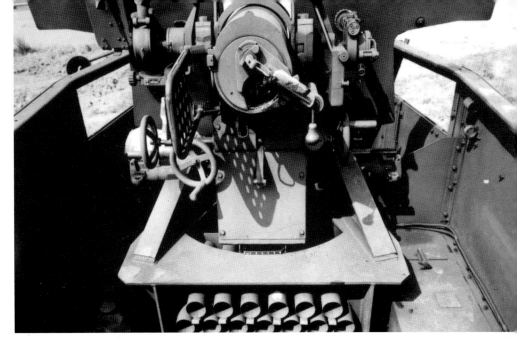

The conversion of the M3 Halftrack to a tank destroyer was relatively simple. The 75mm gun mount was welded to a box structure directly behind the center of the driver's compartment. A rack for nineteen rounds of ammunition was under the gun mount with additional storage space in rear floor bins for forty rounds. The wheels, below the perforated gun recoil guard, are for elevation and traverse. (PAM)

Tests were conducted on this tank destroyer which was fitted with sights for indirect fire support. Once the M3 GMC had been replaced in the tank destroyer role by the M10, it was used by both the Marines and British in the fire support role. The Marines also used it for direct fire support against Japanese bunkers. Occasionally, the M3 GMC was used in the tank destroyer role on those rare instances when Japanese armor came out into the open. (PAM)

M6 37mm Gun Motor Carriage

Another tank destroyer devised just prior to the United States entering the war was the M6 37mm Gun Motor Carriage. Work on this vehicle began in mid-1941 under the test designation T21. This involved mounting a 37mm cannon on the back of a Dodge 3/4 ton weapons carrier. While the weapons carrier was unarmored a large armored shield enclosed the gun mount. Initially this was envisioned as a stopgap measure until the new T22 Gun Motor Carriage was available. A number of different configurations for mounting the gun were tried. It was found that if the gun was mounted in a forward firing configuration the resulting blast from the gun shattered the windshield and caused injury to the driver and front crewman. It was decided to use a rearward firing configuration to solve this problem. This also allowed the vehicle to be positioned for a quick get-away once the gun had been fired and the vehicle's position had been spotted.

The 37mm gun, the standard U.S. anti-tank weapon, had an effective range of 500 yards in this role. It could also fire high explosive (HE) and canister rounds. While the gun mount could traverse 360 degrees this was rarely done for the reasons indicated above. It had an elevation of -10 degrees through +15 degrees. Ammunition for the gun was carried in boxes mounted in the rear body on either side of the tires. Seats were provided for the crew on either side of the truck bed and in the driver's compartment.

The T21 was given the production designation M4 37mm GMC, but this was soon changed to the M6 37mm GMC to avoid confusion with the designation for the carriage of the *towed* 37mm gun. The M6 was manufactured by the Fargo Division of Chrysler and was sometimes known unofficially as the "Fargo". Production began in the spring of 1942 and lasted through the fall, with approximately 5,400 being produced. Used in combat in North Africa, they proved to be a total failure as a tank destroyer. Additional vehicles deployed to the Pacific lasted somewhat longer in the support role. Many were eventually stripped of their gun mounts and converted back to weapons carriers. Those remaining were used primarily for training. Some of the 37mm mounts were later fitted to M2 halftracks to provide additional fire support for mechanized infantry. By the end of the war, the M6 37mm GMC had all but disappeared.

(Above) The T21/M6 was an attempt to mount the 37mm cannon, the Army's standard light anti-tank gun, on the chassis of a Dodge 3/4 ton weapons carrier. A number of different configurations for mounting the gun were tried, but eventually it was decided on a rear firing arrangement since this would allow the vehicle to back into position and thus be ready for a quick exit if its position was discovered. (PAM)

(Below Left) The M6 was unarmored aside from the shield fitted over the 37mm cannon. The rearward firing configuration was also picked over a forward arrangement when it was found that the gun blast could shatter the windshield and cause injury to the crew. (PAM)

(Below) Ammunition for the gun was carried in boxes on either side of the rear wheels. The crew sat in seats above the rear wheels opposite the cannon. The large size of the gun shield is evident and although effective against small arms fire it was easily penetrated by heavier weapons. Called the Fargo, the M6 proved ineffective in combat and quickly disappeared from service, most being converted back to the standard weapons carrier configuration. (PAM)

M10/M10A1 Gun Motor Carriage

Both the M3 and M6 were stopgap measures. What was needed was a specifically designed vehicle for the anti-tank role which had mobility, crew protection, and firepower. The first attempt at this took place in the fall of 1941 when it was proposed to mount an M3 3 inch anti-aircraft gun in the hull of the M3 medium tank which was just then starting to come off the production line. This received the designation T24, but the high silhouette of the mounting and the gun's insufficient range caused the project to be canceled. However, it was decided to further modify the vehicle to carry an M1918 3 inch anti-aircraft gun in a lower mount under the designation T40. Tests on this vehicle led to the decision to put it into production as the M9, but the Tank Destroyer Board rejected the design as not meeting its requirements in mobility and speed. Additionally, there was only a limited number of the guns available for this modification and it was decided to cancel the M9 in the late summer of 1942 before production began.

While the T24 and M9 were not successful, it demonstrated that the use of a medium tank chassis for a tank destroyer was advantageous. As a result in November 1941 plans were drawn up for a new tank destroyer based on the new gasoline powered, cast hull M4A1 tank chassis which was ready for production. The following month a revised design based on the diesel powered, welded hull M4A2 chassis was submitted by officials at Aberdeen Proving Grounds and a wooden mock-up was constructed in January 1942. The design had the M4A2 tank chassis fitted with an open turret mounting a 3 inch gun in place of the tank turret. The tank hull had the same armor protection on the front, but the side armor was reduced to 1 inch. The turret was open both at the top and the rear.

While this design was underway combat reports from the Philippines indicated the advantages which sloped armor provided in terms of protection versus thickness. As a result the Tank Destroyer Board requested a new design using sloped armor on the upper hull to lower the overall height while still providing adequate protection. From the three proposals submitted, one was selected under the test designation T35E1. While this vehicle retained the original turret of the M35, the hull was a completely new design using the sloped armor principle.

The Fisher Tank Division of Chrysler began work on two prototypes in January of 1942 and both were ready for testing in the spring. Results of the tests demonstrated the sloped armor of the T35E1 to be superior to that of the T35. There was concern about the turret when it was found that the cast turret provided less ballistic protection than a turret of rolled armor plate. As a result it was decided to design a new turret of welded construction for use on the production version. In May, following tests, it was decided to accept the T35E1 for production over the T35, with certain modifications. These included reducing the overall armor protection to lessen weight, substituting the new turret for the cast one, replacement of the three piece differential cover with a single piece, and the addition of a second hatch next to the driver for the assistant driver. Provision was made to fit extra armor plates to the turret and front and side hull to provide increased protection in the future. In June of 1942 the new vehicle was redesignated the 3 inch Gun Motor Carriage M10 and approved for production.

A small problem cropped up with the new turret design. As originally envisioned it was to have been hexagonal (six-sided) in shape, but difficulties arose with this design and in order to get the M10 into production as soon as possible a new pentagonal (five sided) shaped turret was devised. By the time the problems with the hexagon turret had been worked out, the pentagon shaped turret was ready for production and it was decided to drop the hexagon turret. With this final design problem solved, the M10 was approved for production and it began to roll off the assembly line in September of 1942. Production would continue until the end of 1943 with nearly 5,000 vehicles being built.

The need for as many tank destroyers as possible as soon as possible led to the decision to have the Ford Motor Company manufacture their own version of the M10 based on the chassis of the gasoline powered M4A3 medium tank under the designation M10A1. The only real distinguishing point between the two were the larger grill doors atop the rear hull of the M10A1. Production of this version ran from October of 1942 to September of 1943 when production was shifted to the Fisher plant where the two models were produced side-by-side. Eventually 1713 M10A1s were produced, including 300 completed without turrets.

The M3 chassis used for the T24 was reworked into the T40 which featured a lower silhouette and a more powerful gun. Test results were acceptable and the T40 was designated the M9. However, the Tank Destroyer Board did not find the vehicle acceptable and the limited number of 3 inch guns available for the conversion made it hardly worth the effort to produce the M9. In addition the new M10, which was far superior, was nearly ready for production. All these factors led to the cancellation of the M9 program in August of 1942. (Hunnicutt)

The T24 was an attempt at building an interim tank destroyer until a specifically designed vehicle could be built. The T24 was a disappointment due to its high silhouette and inadequate range of its gun. It was canceled in April of 1942. (Hunnicutt)

Work had been done on mounting an open-topped turret on the hull of the gasoline powered, cast hull M4A1 medium tank chassis. Later the diesel powered, welded hull M4A2 chassis (above) was substituted minus the bow machine gun and received the designation M35. Additional armor in the form of two plates welded at a 90 degree angle were bolted to the three piece differential housing at the front of the hull. The turret used in the design originally had the rear half of the turret open. (Hunnicutt)

Combat reports from the Philippines indicated the effectiveness of sloping armor for better protection. As a result a reworked hull design emphasizing this was developed under the designation T35E1. The T35E1 was found to be superior to the T35 and was accepted for production with certain modifications. (PAM)

These modifications included a new turret of rolled armored plate, a single piece differential cover, reduction of armor protection, and a second hatch next to the driver for his assistant. Additionally, provisions were made for the attachment of extra armor on the turret and hull sides to large bolts on these surfaces. (PAM)

The new turret was pentagonal with only a small portion of the turret top covered by armor. A mount was provided for a .50 caliber machine gun at the rear of the turret. The small engine access hatch was an easy distinguishing feature of the M10. The track grousers — steel cleats used to improve traction — on the back of the turret were an effort to help balance the heavy weight of the three inch gun but, this proved unsuccessful. (PAM)

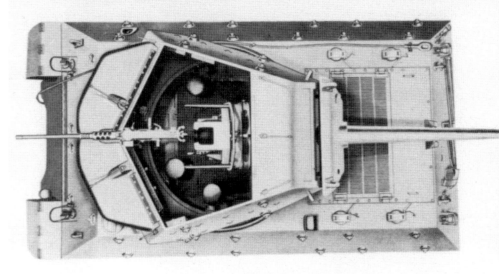

(Above) There was an urgent need for tank destroyers and the chassis of the M4A3 medium tank with a gasoline engine was put into production as the M10A1. Outwardly the two vehicles were identical accept for the rear engine deck. (PAM)

(Below) The final turret design of the M10 provided more room in the interior by angling the sides toward the rear compared to the original design. New counterweights were added which provided additional storage for the crew. This new turret was fitted to both the M10 and M10A1. (USA/NA)

(Above) The only real distinguishing characteristic between the M10A1 and the M10 was the larger engine grill of the M10A1. This vehicle features the V shaped turret counterweights which replaced small counterweights that had been tried when the track grousers failed to solve the balance problem. (Hunnicutt)

11

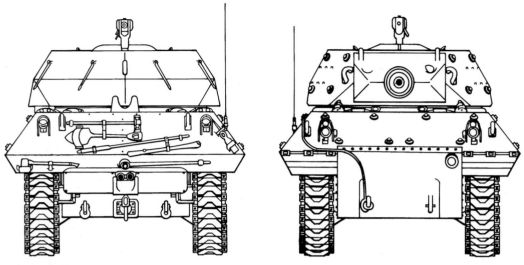
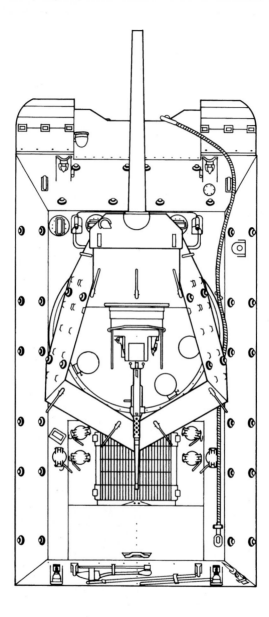

M10 GMC

Length:...................22 Feet, 5 Inches
Width:.....................10 Feet
Height:...................9 Feet, 6 Inches
Weight (Combat):. 65,000 Pounds
Gun:.......................3 Inch, M7
Rounds:.................54
Speed::..................30 Mph
Range:...................200 Miles
Crew:.....................5

The M10 Series

The diesel powered M10 and the gasoline powered M10Al were almost identical externally aside from the top rear engine doors. The M10 was powered by a GM 6046 12 cylinder, twin, diesel in-line engine while the M10A1 featured a Ford GAA 8 cylinder 4 cycle gasoline powerplant. Their suspensions were the standard vertical volute spring type with twelve wheels in six sets of bogies. The drive sprocket was at the front with a rear idler wheel and six return rollers, one at the rear of each bogie unit.

Armor protection was relatively thin with the gun mantlet being the thickest at 2.25 inches. The front hull armor varied in thickness with the lower hull being 2 inches while the upper hull was 1.5 inches. The hull sides and rear were 1 inch on the lower and .75 inch on the upper angles. Top armor varied between .75 inch (front) and .375 inch (rear). The turret sides and rear were 1 inch with .75 inch on top. When fully loaded the M10 was 33 tons while the M10A1 was 32 tons.

The main armament of the vehicles was an M7 3 inch gun in an M5 mount in an open top turret. The turret could be rotated through 360 degrees with elevations between -10 through +30 degrees. The maximum firing rate was 15 rounds per minute and 54 rounds of ammunition could be carried. The gun could fire armor piercing (AP), high explosive (HE), canister, and smoke rounds. Maximum effective range for the AP rounds was approximately 1,000 yards. Additionally, provision for a flexible, pintle mounted .50 caliber machine gun was made on the rear of the turret.

The crew consisted of five men, the commander, driver, assistant driver, gunner, and loader. The driver was seated in the left front hull with the assistant to his right. Each had their own hatches for entry or exit. The remainder of the crew were positioned in the open turret with the commander seated on the right of the gun, the gunner on the left, and the loader positioned at the rear.

The basic shape of the two models changed very little over the life of the production run. The only major outward change was in the shape of the turret which went through a number of modifications and design changes to improve balance which was found to be a problem with the early production models. Tests had indicated that the turret was unbalanced due to the heavy gun and several attempts were made to solve the problem. Initially, track grousers were fitted to the rear of the turret and the .50 caliber machine gun was positioned at the rear corner. This did not solve the balance problem, however, and early units were often modified in the field with makeshift counterweights being welded to the rear of the turret. Eventually two large triangular shaped counterweights were devised and fitted to the turret rear to solve the balance problem. These weighed a total of 3,600 pounds and were fitted to new vehicles coming off the production line. Late in the production life of the series a new turret was designed which provided more working room and incorporated a new counterweight. This new turret had the upper part of the rear side extended back which squared off the rear of the turret and gave additional space for the crew. This new counterweight also provided more storage of gear which helped alleviate some of the crowding in the interior.

In addition to changes in the turret, there were changes to the interior which were incorporated during production. These were mostly of a minor nature and caused no outward change in the vehicle's appearance. Initially the M10 had only sights for direct firing, but later provisions were made for indirect firing also. Some work was done on changing the manual traverse mechanism, but before this was ready for installation production wound down and it was never installed. One of the more obvious problems which was highlighted in combat was the lack of overhead protection for the crew. Both in Europe and the Pacific the M10 was found to be vulnerable when used in close confines such as the hedgerows in Normandy and in the jungles of the Pacific. In Europe this became even more of a problem as fighting progressed through towns in the drive toward Germany. In the close confines of street fighting the crews were often exposed to snipers, grenades, and overhead shell bursts which could be deadly. Some units made improvised overhead protection using sandbags, wood, and in a few cases, jury rigged armored enclosures. There were no modifications on the production line to address this problem and it was to remain a major concern to the end of the war.

M10 TURRET EVOLUTION

| **Original Turret** | **Early Production Turret** | **Mid-Production Turret** | **Late Production Turret** |

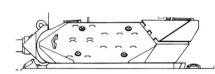
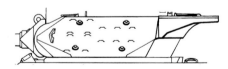
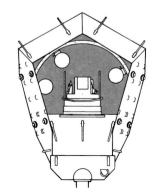
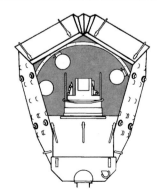
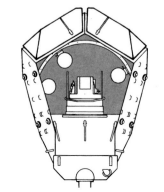
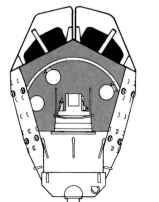

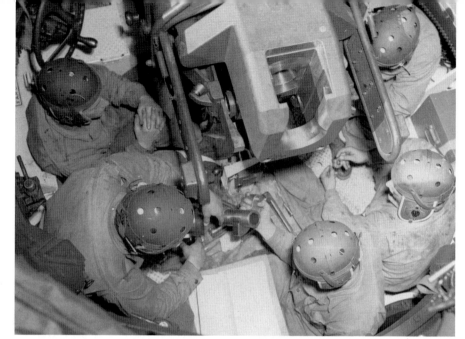

The main armament of the M10/M10A1 was a three inch gun mounted in the revolving turret. The gunner's sight is to the left while the breech block is in the center foreground. Directly above the gun breech area is the travel lock which helps keep the gun stationary when the vehicle is on the move. (USA/NA)

One of the main drawbacks of the M10 was its open turret top. This proved a liability during combat in towns and dense vegetation or jungle. No satisfactory solution was ever developed to rectify this problem aside from modifications made in the field. This M10's turret has been fitted with a field modification designed by the 536th Ordnance Heavy Maintenance Company of the Seventh Army in early 1945. This is the final production version of the M10 turret which can be identified by the squared off rear corners and the counterweights. (USA/NA)

The turret interior was quite cramped on the M10, although only the commander, gunner, and loader should have been in the turret during operations. The crew is wearing the standard US Army issue helmets which were designed only to protect the head against coming into contact with hard objects. They offered no ballistic protection whatsoever. (USA/NA)

The M10 turret and hull plates were welded. The last production turret had the rear squared off and a new counterweight added. The counterweight was longer and had a scalloped undersurface. The use of stars for identification under the overhang of the turret counterweight was not widely used. (USA/NA)

Achilles

The M10 was supplied under Lend-Lease to the British who utilized it in the anti-tank and indirect fire roles. In British service, these vehicles were known as "Wolverines". In order to improve its anti-tank potential, it was decided to replace the American 3 inch gun with the more potent British 17 pounder Mark V. Two lugs were added to the gun's breech which allowed it to be fitted into the turret without major problems. Although the gun breech did cause the gun to be unbalanced, the smaller diameter of the gun barrel necessitated welding a collar on the gun shield to compensate for this smaller diameter. This helped to offset the balance problem and with the addition of a counterweight at the end of the barrel the problem was completely solved. Other changes included cutting an elongated hole in the gun shield on the left side for a new direct sighting telescope. Interior stowage was also rearranged to meet British equipment and crew requirements. The 17 pounder could be elevated from -5 through +20 degrees, slightly less than the movement of the US 3 inch gun, but this was more than compensated for with its outstanding anti-tank performance. A total of 50 rounds of ammunition could be carried with 6 rounds being stored in ready racks in the turret and the remainder in the hull sponsons — that part of the hull sides immediately above the tracks.

These 17 pounder upgunned vehicles were designated "Achilles" and it appears there were two versions. A few vehicles with the early production turrets were fitted with the 17 pounder gun and were known as "Achilles Ic", but few of these seem to have been converted. The most common version was the "Achilles IIc" which was based on the final production turret with a roomier interior and the revised counterweights on the turret rear. This version did not have the fittings for the addition of extra armor plate.

The British realized that there was a critical need for an upgunned version of the M10 and, as a result, fitted many of their late model M10 with the very potent 17 pounder Mk V. Aside from minor modifications to the gun mount, little else was needed to mount the gun in the M10 turret. To balance the gun a counterweight was added just behind the muzzle brake. (Hunnicutt)

The smaller diameter of the 17 pound gun barrel compared to the 3 inch gun required the installation of a special collar to compensate for the size difference. A new casting was welded over the hole to solve the problem which, along with the barrel counterweight, also helped to balance the gun. (Hunnicutt)

M10 GMC (Late Turret)

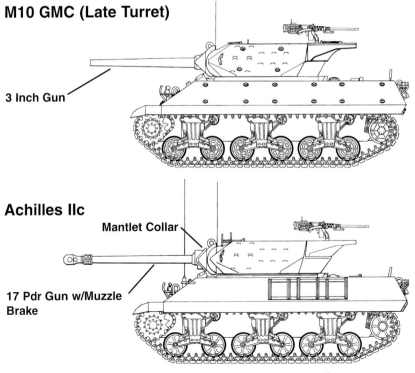

3 Inch Gun

Achilles IIc

Mantlet Collar

17 Pdr Gun w/Muzzle Brake

T72

In March of 1943, in an attempt to lower the overall weight of the vehicle, it was decided to develop a new turret for the M10 fitted with a 76mm gun. The 76mm gun had the same armor penetration as the 3 inch gun used in the M10 but was substantially lighter. If the new turret could be efficiently designed there were hopes for a weight saving of almost three tons. This new design received the designation T72.

The new turret was a lighter version of the one used on the T23 medium tank but with an open top and much thinner armor. A small bustle was added at the rear of the turret to balance out the weight of the barrel. Due to the smaller size of the 76mm ammunition, 27 rounds could be carried in the bustle at the rear of the turret along with 72 in the sponson racks. This more than doubled the number of rounds which could be carried from 45 to 99.

An order was given for two test models to be manufactured and these were fitted to two gasoline powered M10A1 chassis. Both of these were delivered to Aberdeen in April of 1943 and put through various field tests. The weight savings amounted to a little over two tons, still quite substantial. The new turret was roomier and the traverse and elevation controls were more accessible. Of course the cost for this was also some reduction in armor protection, but this was felt to be acceptable.

While this development was going on, work was also being done on the new T70 (later designated the M18 Hellcat) mounting the same 76mm gun. Due to its torsion bar suspension, which was superior to the M10 vertical volute suspension, it was decided to cancel the T72 project in early 1944 in favor of the T70. Had there been a need for a 76mm gun turret for the M10 series it was stipulated that the new turret from the T70/M18 be used.

(Above) In early 1943 it was decided to design a new turret for the M10 which carried the 76mm gun. While both weapons had the same penetration power, the 76mm gun was lighter and there was hope for a substantial weight savings. This version received the designation T72. The new turret was a lightweight version of the T23 design being produced for the M4 medium tank. The chassis used for the conversion was the M10A1. (Hunnicutt)

(Below) The shape of the new turret was very different from the M10 with its angular look and rear bustle. The smaller size of the 76mm ammunition allowed over twice as many rounds to be carried compared to the M10. However, the new T70/M18 Hellcat was deemed a better vehicle overall and work on the T72 was halted in February of 1944. (Hunnicutt)

M36, M36B1, and M36B2

By the time the M10 went into production, newer German tanks were beginning to appear on the battlefield with more armor protection. This trend toward increased armor indicated that the 3 inch gun of the M10 might not be sufficient against the newer German tanks. With this in mind, officials looked into the possibility of mounting a 90mm anti-aircraft gun in both the M10 and M10A1 as well as in tanks. A modified 90mm gun was mounted in the pilot model M10 during the summer of 1942. While the gun weighed about 300 pounds more than the 3 inch gun there were no major problems in fitting it into the turret. As with the 3 inch gun there was a balance problem and, due to the size of the 90mm rounds, fewer could be carried. These were not considered insurmountable problems. It was felt the balance problem could be fixed with additional counterweights on the turret rear, but the optimum solution was to design a new turret with a power traverse mechanism.

M36

Work on a wooden turret mock-up was begun by Chevrolet during the early spring of 1943. The completed mock-up was sent to Ford where two M10A1s were fitted with mild steel mock-ups. Following tests at Aberdeen and Ft. Knox, the designation T71 was given to vehicles based on the M10A1 chassis, and T71E1 to those based on the M10 chassis. The new turret shape differed significantly from the M10 with a more rounded gun shield and rounded turret sides. At the rear of the turret a large bustle housing ready ammunition rounds replaced the counterweights of the M10. Turret armor all around was thicker than the M10, particularly on the bustle which at some points was 5 inches thick to protect the ammunition.

The crew positions were also altered. The gunner was moved to the right side of the gun while the loader moved to the left of the gun. The commander sat behind the gunner. Due to the weight of the gun and turret a power traverse mechanism was incorporated into the new turret along with a manual system. A ring mount for a .50 caliber machine gun was fitted on the left side of the turret.

Following tests at Aberdeen and Ft. Knox, a number of minor changes were requested by Army officials. These included revising the internal ammunition storage in the sponsons, making minor adjustments to turret equipment, and removal of the machine gun ring mount in favor of a pedestal atop the bustle. These changes were incorporated on the number 2 pilot model which was sent to Ft. Knox and then to Ft. Hood for additional tests. Again, minor changes were recommended, such as the addition of a muzzle brake and different ammunition to reduce muzzle and flash blast, and a better gun sight.

By November of 1943 the design for the turret had been finalized and Fisher was given a contract for 500 of the new vehicles initially converting the M10A1s already on the production line. Since nearly 200 of these were near completion with their turrets already in place, only 300 were available for conversion from the M10A1s to the 90mm M36s. To meet the needs for additional vehicles M10A1s were taken from the field and depots to provide the necessary chassis. Due to their work load Fisher could not handle this additional work. The Massey Harris Company was called in and completed an order for 500 by the end of 1944. The T71 was redesignated the M36 in June of 1944.

By this time the invasion of Europe had taken place and during the early stages of the Normandy battle the Army found out just how inadequate the 75mm and 76mm armed M4 Sherman was against German tanks like the Panther. A cry went out for a more powerful vehicle to deal with the German armor threat and the 90mm armed M36 was rushed into action. The demand for the vehicle was so great that an additional contract for 413 M36s was given to the American Locomotive Company to convert M10A1s to this configuration. Even this was not enough to satisfy the demand and a way had to be found to provide additional vehicles as quickly as possible.

M36B1

The pressing need for more heavily armed tank destroyers led to the decision to fit the new 90mm turret onto the standard hull of an M4A3 Sherman tank. Aside from rearranging internal storage to handle the larger ammunition, there were no other changes made in what was basically a very simple conversion. This version was designated the M36B1 and classified in October as Substitute Standard. With the M4A3 armor thickness this vehicle was the most heavily armored US tank destroyer used during World War II. It was also the only one to have a bow machine gun which was retained during the conversion process. Fisher completed 187 of these vehicles by the end of 1944.

M36B2

Production of the M36 and M36B1 terminated at the end of 1944 but the need for additional vehicles was so great that production started up once again in the spring of 1945. However, the supply of M10A1s was soon exhausted. In place of these the M10 was substituted and these vehicles received the designation M36B2. The most noticeable change which was incorporated on these was the addition of overhead cover as a result of reports from the battlefield. A series of folding flaps allowed the crew to button up when in danger from small arms or artillery fire yet did not cause a serious reduction in all around vision. A large muzzle brake was fitted and numerous minor internal changes were made. This version was produced by American Locomotive which made 672 and Montreal Locomotive which manufactured 52.

In an effort to upgrade the armament of the M10 a new turret fitted with a 90mm gun was developed and tested on an M10 and M10A1 hull under the respective designations T71E1 and T71. The new turret was very different from the M10 turret, featuring a new mantlet, a rounded configuration, and a much larger rear turret bustle. This pilot model of the T71 featured a ring mount for the .50 caliber machine gun which was deleted on the production model. (Hunnicutt)

(Above) The 90mm gun gave the T71 the best anti-tank capability of any US vehicle in service at the time, aside from the T26 which was still under development. The large bustle at the rear of the turret was used for storage of the large 90mm rounds. The ring mount for the .50 caliber machine gun has been removed from the turret by this time in the evaluation. (PAM)

(Below) The 90mm armed T71 went into production as the M36 in the spring of 1944. Despite the M36's new gun and turret, there was a strong family resemblance between the M36 and the earlier M10A1. The main external differences were the shape of the mantlet and the extended bustle of the M36. The 90mm gun of the M36 came as a nasty surprise to German tankers, especially since it was difficult to distinguish between the two vehicles at a distance. (USA/NA)

(Above) Like the M10 the T71 turret was open-topped with the same problems. The larger engine hatches of the M10A1 chassis can be barely seen under the rear turret bustle of this pilot T71. (PAM)

There was such a critical need for the new 90mm armed M36 in Europe that 187 M4A3 medium tanks were converted to tank destroyers under the designation M36B1. Aside from internal storage rearrangement the conversion was relatively simple. Although the height of the M36B1 conversion was higher than the M36 it was more heavily armored and was the only American tank destroyer to carry a hull mounted machine gun. (PAM)

M10 GMC (Late Production)

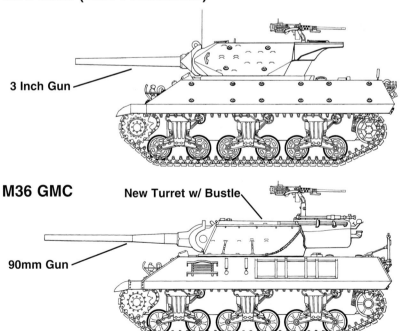

3 Inch Gun

M36 GMC

New Turret w/ Bustle

90mm Gun

The M36B1 was classified as Substitute Standard and proved to be an easy way to quickly get additional 90mm guns into the European theater. The 90mm gun could be fitted with a muzzle brake, but this was rarely seen during the war due to the time involved in fitting it and its related equipment. The X shaped frame of the turret top was a brace for a foul weather tarp. (PAM)

Despite the efforts made to provide the M36 to the troops in the field there were not enough of the M10A1 chassis left to fill the need. As a result in the spring of 1945 the M10 was substituted on the production line under the designation M36B2. One feature which was added to the M36B2 was armored hatches on the roof to alleviate the problem of the opened topped turret. This closed turret modification for the M36B2 was tested on a standard M36 chassis. (PAM)

The new armored cover had three hatches at the rear which were attached to the rigid front portion. The hatches swung forward, although some turrets seem to have had the right hatch fixed to swing to the rear. The wider engine hatches of this M36 indicate that it was the pilot model for the M36B2 turret. (PAM)

Folding hatches and end flaps on the new overhead cover allowed the crew to retain adequate visibility from inside the turret. The M36 was fitted with a muzzle brake. M36s also featured extended track end connectors which increased the track width, reduced ground pressure, and improved the cross country mobility. (PAM)

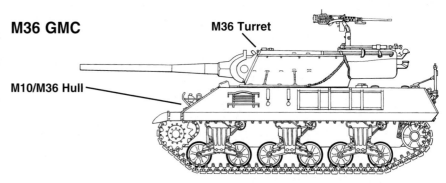

M36 GMC

M36 Turret

M10/M36 Hull

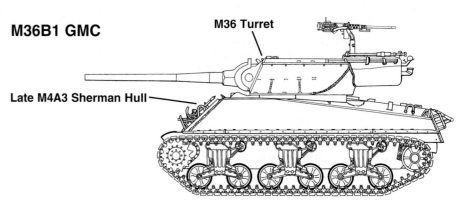

M36B1 GMC

M36 Turret

Late M4A3 Sherman Hull

M36B2 Overhead Hatch Kit

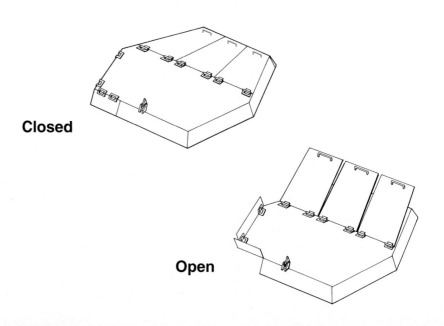

Closed

Open

M18 Hellcat

During the early part of the war there was a great deal of interest in developing a lightweight, highly mobile tank destroyer. Some work was done on mounting the 3 inch gun on the M3 Stuart light tank chassis under the test designations T50, T56, and T57, but the weight of the gun overloaded the chassis. Following this, a 75mm gun was fitted in the turret of the M8 Howitzer Motor Carriage, which was based on the later M5 Stuart light tank. Tests were encouraging and plans were made to produce this vehicle on a limited basis until a new project already under development was ready for service. However, it was realized that the new vehicle would be ready before the modified M8 could be delivered in sufficient numbers so the M8 program was cancelled.

In late 1941 there was a proposal to mount a 37mm cannon in an open-topped turret on the chassis of the M9 light airborne tank under the designation T42. By the spring of 1942, however, the Ordnance Department realized that a heavier weapon was needed against German armor and ordered the 37mm gun replaced by the new 57mm cannon based on the British 6 pounder. The new design received the designation T49 and two pilot models were constructed by General Motors Buick Division. The first T49 pilot vehicle was ready by July and sent to Aberdeen for tests. Tests showed that the vehicle was not able to achieve the desired speed due to its torque converter, however, the Christie type suspension was found to provide a smooth ride without shedding the new center-guide tracks at high speeds over rough terrain.

While these tests were underway, Tank Destroyer Command indicated its preference for the 75mm gun which led the Ordnance officials to have the second pilot model fitted with a 75mm gun instead of the 57mm gun. This vehicle received the designation T67 and the original pilot was returned to be fitted with the larger gun. The second pilot arrived at Aberdeen for testing in November of 1942 and featured an open topped turret and redesigned front hull which had the original bow machine gun eliminated. The 75mm gun proved satisfactory, however the powerplant was considered inadequate and it was recommended that a more powerful engine be fitted. During testing the 75mm gun was replaced with the new 76mm M1 cannon which provided better armor penetration. As a result of these tests it was decided to cancel the T67 and design a new vehicle based on its general parameters and armed with the 76mm gun under the designation T70. An order for six pilot models was given in January of 1943 to General Motors, which had the first pilot model ready in the spring.

All of the other pilot models were ready for testing by July and these began at Aberdeen and Ft. Hood. The main changes between the T70 and the T67 were the replacement of the original twin Buick engines with a Continental R-975-C1 radial engine and the movement of the transmission and final drive to the front of the vehicle for better balance. An interesting feature was the mounting of both the engine and the transmission and final drive on rails for easy removal and service. The T70 retained the dual road wheel configuration of the T67, but torsion bars replaced the Christie type coiled spring suspension.

Tests showed that overall the T70 was a very fine vehicle, although some problems did come to light. The front shock absorber proved too weak to handle the weight and a second one was added. Eventually a new, stronger shock absorber was designed which alleviated the problem. Short track life was also a problem and work was done to increase its longevity. The 76mm gun was centered on the test vehicles but this was found to make removal of the gun difficult. As a result the gun was moved two inches to the right which solved the removal problem as well as giving the gunner additional room. A slight bulge on the left side of the turret was also eliminated as a result of this shift.

With these bugs worked out, production began almost immediately at the General Motors Buick plant in July of 1943 and ran until October of 1944 when the last of 2,507 vehicles was completed. In March 1944 the T70 was redesignated the 76mm Gun Motor Carriage M18 and later received the nickname "Hellcat".

The M18 was one of the better armored designs produced in the United States during the war. Its most prominent asset was its phenomenal speed, upwards of 50 miles an hour. When compared to the mid-20 MPH range of the M4/M10/M36 family and the low 30s for the M24 light tank this was outstanding. Of course this high speed was only achieved due to the relatively thin armor on the vehicle which at its thickest was only one inch on the front casting. Elsewhere the armor was usually around half an inch thick on vertical surfaces, not a lot against the heavy guns carried by German tanks. However, coupled with this high speed was the good armor penetration power of the 76mm cannon. This combination gave the M18 a very good chance of survival in combat as long as the crew had the ability to fire and run rather than sit and try to slug it out with the opposition.

The crew of the M18 consisted of five members: the driver on the left and his assistant on the right. The loader sat on the right side of the turret with the gunner on the left. The commander was positioned right behind the gunner. The turret held 9 ready rounds to the right of the gun in a small rack while an additional 18 were stored in each sponson for a total of 45. The only additional armament was a .50 caliber machine gun in a ring mount at the left rear of the turret.

There was a great deal of interest early in the war for developing a tank destroyer based on the M3/M5 Stuart light tank chassis. The first of these was the T56 which featured a rear mounted 3 inch gun. The weight of the gun proved too much for the chassis and in the next version, the T57, even the removal of the gun shield and a more powerful engine could not alleviate the problem. Here, the pilot model of the T56 awaits field tests at Aberdeen Proving Ground in November 1942. Both the T56 and T57 were canceled in early 1943. (Hunnicutt)

by the commander's position.

During the production run very few changes were incorporated into the design. The first 685 vehicles were returned to the factory during the spring and summer of 1944 to incorporate a new gear ratio. Of these, 640 were modified to the M39 armored utility vehicle by removing the turret, modifying the interior to carry troops, and moving the .50 caliber machine gun forward. The M18 initially used the M1A1 gun which lacked a muzzle brake. Later, the M1A1C and M1A2 guns were employed. Both the M1A1C and M1A2 could be fitted with a muzzle brake. The M1A2 also had rifling with a higher rate of twist which improved its accuracy. All three guns were in regular service use through the winter and spring of 1945

Aside from the M39 mentioned above there were no other production models of the M18 produced during the war. Some work was done on experimental variants such as an amphibious version for which two test models were produced. The T86 and the T86E1 differed mainly in how they were propelled in the water, the former by its tracks, and the latter by a propeller. The hulls were modified above the sponsons with a new lightweight hull for buoyancy. The turrets were moved up 30 inches on the new hull and an elevation stabilizer was fitted to the gun mount. A third pilot model was also made, but this model carried a 105mm howitzer. This evolved out of the T88 model of the standard M18 which had been fitted with a 105mm howitzer for use as a support weapon. None of these experimental models got beyond the test stages

By the spring of 1945 the new M3 90mm gun was finally getting into widespread service . In an effort to fit it to the M18, an M36 turret was mounted on a Hellcat at Aberdeen Proving Grounds to test its feasibility. The only modification needed was to raise the floor of the turret and slip rings by two inches along with ammunition stowage rearrangement. Tests showed that the heavier gun did not adversely affect the chassis if a muzzle brake was fitted to the gun barrel. To compensate for the increase in weight wider tracks were later fitted as was a gun travel lock from an M26 Pershing. The tentative designation for this model was the 90mm Gun Motor Carriage M18, but the end of the war in August of 1945 ended the development of this very promising combination.

As with the M36 there was also an attempt to provide overhead protection, by installing an overhead plate with hatches for the commander and loader. Armored side flaps could be raised to allow a full 360 degree view for the crew. The end of the war also brought an end to this development and no production of the overhead kit was undertaken.

The T56/T57 was followed by the M8A1, the unofficial designation for an M8 Howitzer Motor Carriage fitted with a 75mm gun. It was cancelled when the superior T70/M18 was ready for service (Hunnicutt)

The inadequacies of the 37mm gun led to the 57mm armed T49 with an enclosed turret and bow machine gun. In testing the T49 did not fulfill the requirements of the Army, although the new suspension system was favorably received. (Hunnicutt)

(Below) The second pilot model was ordered with a 75mm gun and designated the T67. It had a redesigned hull and an open topped turret. The bow machine gun was eliminated. It was found to be underpowered. (Hunnicutt)

It was decided to cancel the T67 and concentrate on a new modification, the T70 which featured a more powerful engine and a 76mm gun in place of the 75mm cannon of the T67. By the spring of 1943 the first pilot was ready, with the remaining five being delivered by July for testing. This is the third pilot and shows the influence of the T49/T67 models. The bulge on the turret side was due to the width of the 76mm gun mount. Later, when the gun was moved off-center the bulge was eliminated. The ring mounted .50 caliber machine gun was incorporated into the production model. (Hunnicutt)

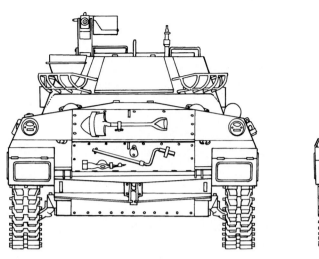

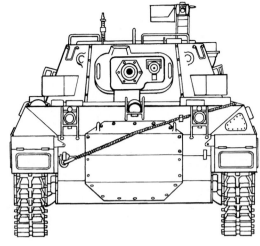

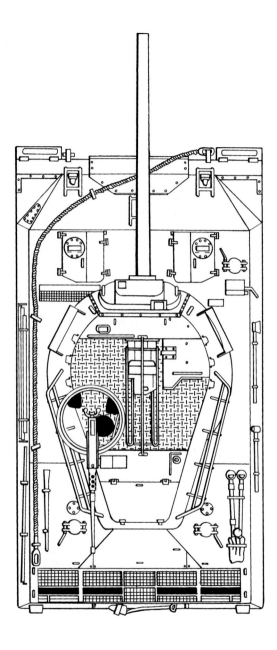

M18 Hellcat

Length:.....................21 Feet, 10 Inches
Width:.......................9 Feet, 9 Inches
Height:.....................8 Feet, 5 Inches
Weight (Combat):...40,000 Pounds
Gun:.........................76mm M1A1, M1A1C, M1A2
Rounds:...................45
Speed:.....................55 Mph
Range:.....................150 Miles
Crew:.......................5

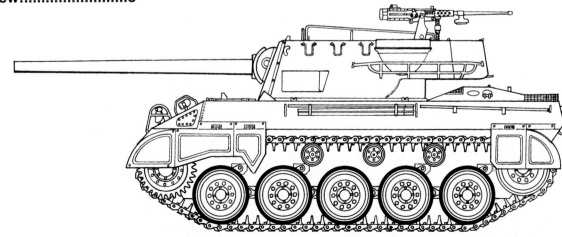

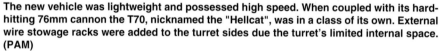

The new vehicle was lightweight and possessed high speed. When coupled with its hard-hitting 76mm cannon the T70, nicknamed the "Hellcat", was in a class of its own. External wire stowage racks were added to the turret sides due the turret's limited internal space. (PAM)

Like all other production tank destroyers the T70 featured an open-topped turret. The 76mm gun took up most of the turret center, causing a fairly tight fit. Hatches for the driver and his assistant and the open turret top made for easy entry and escape if needed. (PAM)

The rear of the turret featured a prominent overhang which housed radio equipment and a large storage bin at the back. Spare tracks were carried on the end of the turret bustle. A variety of tools were carried on the rear of the engine compartment. The engine, mounted on rails, could be pulled out the rear for easy service or replacement. (PAM)

After tests at various facilities in the U.S. a small number of T70s were sent overseas to Italy for combat tests. These tests resulted in favorable comments from the crews, especially concerning the vehicles high speed. By the time these tests were completed the T70 had been accepted for service under the designation M18 as indicated on the side of this Hellcat at Aberdeen Proving Grounds in the summer of 1944. Early production Hellcats were not be fitted with a muzzle brake. (Hunnicutt)

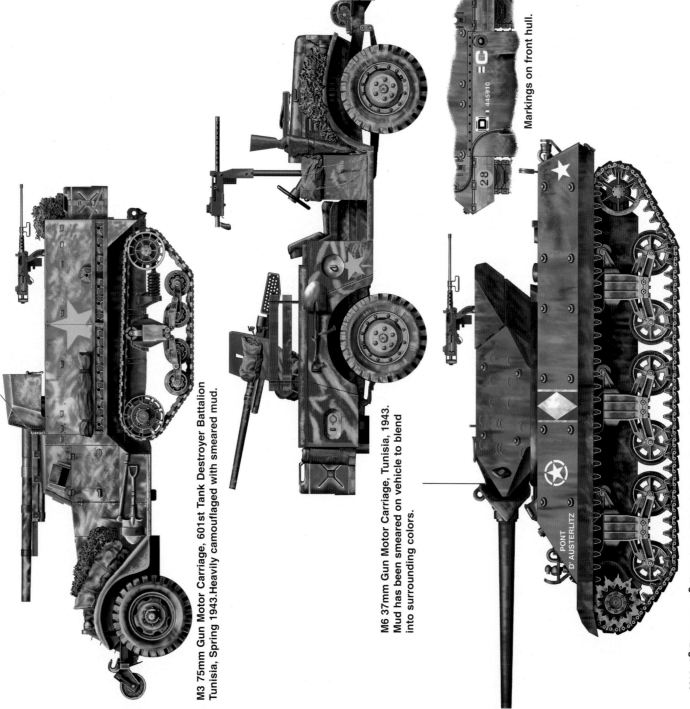

M3 75mm Gun Motor Carriage, 601st Tank Destroyer Battalion Tunisia, Spring 1943.Heavily camouflaged with smeared mud.

M6 37mm Gun Motor Carriage, Tunisia, 1943. Mud has been smeared on vehicle to blend into surrounding colors.

Markings on front hull.

M10, 2e Dragons, 4e Escadron, French Army, France, 1944.

M36, 2nd Cavalry, Third Army, Oberwesel, Germany, March 1945.

445910

28

PONT D' AUSTERLITZ

U S A 40191415

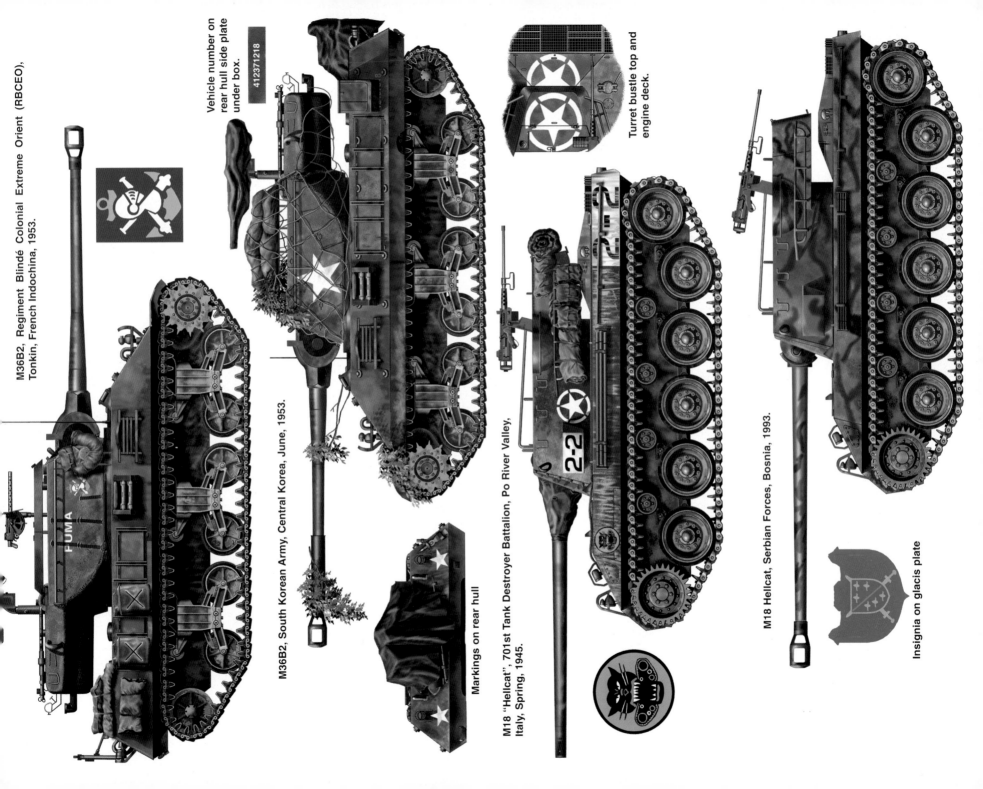

M36B2, Regiment Blindé Colonial Extreme Orient (RBCEO), Tonkin, French Indochina, 1953.

Vehicle number on rear hull side plate under box.

412371218

M36B2, South Korean Army, Central Korea, June, 1953.

Markings on rear hull

Turret bustle top and engine deck.

M18 "Hellcat", 701st Tank Destroyer Battalion, Po River Valley, Italy, Spring, 1945.

2-2

M18 Hellcat, Serbian Forces, Bosnia, 1993.

Insignia on glacis plate

The M18 Hellcat carried three different 76mm cannons, the M1A1, M1A1C, and M1A2. The M1A1C and M1A2 began to appear in the fall of 1944 and could be equipped with muzzle brakes like the one fitted to this late model M18. When not fitted with a muzzle brake a thread protector was fitted to guard against damage and corrosion. All three guns were in regular use through the winter and spring of 1945. (Hunnicutt)

Installing an M36 turret on the M18 dwarfed the small chassis of the M18, but no major technical problems arose from the conversion. However, when the 90mm gun was fired, the recoil caused the M18 to move backwards almost two feet! When fired to the side, the Hellcat rocked violently, much worse than when fired to the front. Fitting a muzzle brake reduced this recoil problem to only minor movement overall. (Hunnicutt)

The success of the 90mm gun in combat led the Army to mount the turret from an M36 on the M18 chassis. This was accomplished with very few modifications and resulted in a lightweight gun carriage with a tremendously powerful weapon coupled with high speed and mobility. (Hunnicutt)

The large bustle of the M36 turret covered most of the rear deck. To handle the increase in weight wider tracks were later fitted to reduce ground pressure. An M26 travel lock was also fitted to the rear deck. The 90mm "Super Hellcat" proved to be a very effective conversion and would have been placed in service had the war with Japan not ended in September 1945. With the surrender of Japan, there was no need for this vehicle and the project was canceled in the fall of 1945. (Hunnicutt)

Combat Service

The new Tank Destroyer Command had as it's motto *"Seek, Strike, and Destroy"*, but how this was to be achieved was still under study. The first use of tank destroyers by American forces came not against the Germans but against the Japanese in the Philippines. In the fall of 1941, with war clouds gathering over the Pacific, an effort was made to bolster US defenses in the islands. Included in these reinforcements were 50 of the new pre-production M3 75mm GMCs. The M3 75mm GMCs were formed into a self-propelled artillery unit to support the Provisional Tank Group which was equipped with M3 Stuart light tanks. Primarily used as artillery, the new vehicles were also employed as needed to bolster defenses and support troops against possible Japanese tank attacks. It is unclear whether they actually destroyed any Japanese armor, but they did prove to be valuable as mobile artillery throughout the campaign. A number of captured vehicles were refurbished and used by the Japanese and some were later encountered and destroyed by American armor when U.S. forces returned in 1944.

The Philippine experience highlighted the technical deficiencies of the M3 75mm GMC. Gradually, however, tactics were worked out and laid down in the Tank Destroyer Manual. In Field Manual (FM) 18-5 it was stated, *"Tank Destroyer units are especially designed for offensive action against hostile armored forces."* This was to be done in cooperation with other combat arms such as artillery and armor, but the tank destroyers were to be *"capable of semi-independent action."* Enemy armor was to be destroyed by offensive action based on vigorous reconnaissance to locate enemy tanks and to attack them from advantageous positions. To compensate for their thin armor, the tank destroyers were to use speed, mobility, cover, and superior observation to offset the enemy tanks' superior armor protection.

On the other side of the world the first encounters with German forces took place during the fighting in North Africa. Six tank destroyer battalions were deployed there, all but one of them being equipped with the 75mm M3 and 37mm M6 GMCs, while the other had the new 3 inch M10. Unfortunately, in the heat of battle, FM 18-5 suffered and results initially were not favorable. The M6 proved to be worthless and was quickly withdrawn from service. The M3 75mm GMCs were employed in a number of roles for which they were neither intended nor equipped to function. Used in an aggressive role, they suffered severe losses. The M3s were often used offensively in the open against German armor with heavy losses. In some instances, they were literally used as tanks, a role for which they were definitely not suited. It was not until they were in their intended role with the proper tactics that they achieved some success. During the battle of El Guettar the 601st Tank Destroyer Battalion, in support of the 1st Infantry Division ("The Big Red One") helped repel an attack by the 10th Panzer Division during which it claimed 30 enemy tanks knocked out, including two Tiger Is. However, the unit lost 21 of their GMCs, not the best of ratios. This was the high point of the M3's career as a tank destroyer and as quickly as possible they were withdrawn from service and converted back to the standard halftrack configuration and replaced by M10s for the invasion of Sicily and Italy. Gradually, the survivors' reports filtered back to headquarters and revisions and clarifications were made in FM 18-5 which helped to change tactics. Unfortunately, many units possessing tank destroyers continued to use them incorrectly, much to the chagrin of the tank destroyer units.

The circumstances for which the tank destroyer force had been formed was rarely encountered during the Italian campaign. Designed as a means of stopping hordes of German tanks which had ruptured a defensive line, it slowly became apparent that this was not occurring. As a result tank destroyer units were parceled out as the need arose. Gradually battalions were assigned almost on a permanent basis to infantry and tank divisions where they were used to provide direct support fire or as self-propelled artillery, roles they had obviously not been intended for. In particular the open top configuration of the M10 turret made it unsuitable for employment where there was a danger of artillery or mortar fire or when snipers were active. Suggestions were made to replace the tank destroyers with regular M4s which were considered more versatile, but these suggestions were vetoed by General McNair who remained a supporter of his pet project despite the flaws which had been found in both tank destroyer equipment and doctrine.

By the invasion of France, the role of the tank destroyer was being seriously questioned. As in Italy they were parceled out as needed, but there was one significant difference. In the Normandy area the U.S. Army encountered the newest German armor and were shocked to find out that the 75mm armed M4 Sherman was hard pressed to survive against the Panther and Tiger I and II let alone knock them out. The M10s were the only vehicle with a gun which could take them on until the newer M18 and M4s armed with the 76mm gun came on the scene. This led to the rushed delivery of the M36 armed with the 90mm cannon to help redress the situation. However, the flat trajectory of the tank destroyer guns made them ideal support weapons against bunkers and machine gun nests in the *bocage* (hedgerows) of the Normandy countryside. But again the lack of overhead cover made them particularly vulnerable to sniper, mortar, and artillery fire in the close confines of the hedgerows.

When the Allies broke out of Normandy, the tank destroyers were employed much like Sherman tanks, pushing ahead, often covered with infantry, providing support as needed, and occasionally fending off German counterattacks when the enemy had a chance regroup. Due to the nature of the campaign, they were rarely used in their intended role. This changed dramatically in December of 1944 when the Germans turned loose their Ardennes Offensive. This was one of the few instances where U.S. forces faced the kind of attack that the tank destroyer force had been specifically formed to handle — a massed tank assault. But, since they were not under the control of a central command, the tank destroyer units could not be concentrated against the German breakthrough. However, they did play a vital role in the defenses of St. Vith and especially at Bastogne where they were instrumental in helping to hold the town against repeated German attacks. Eventually with the help of air support the German breakthrough was contained, then repulsed with severe losses, to the German Army.

The "Battle of the Bulge", as the German attack in the Ardennes became known, was the swansong of the German *panzer* forces. From this time on it was rare for American and Allied forces to encounter concentrations of German armor. Tank destroyers were used chiefly in the direct fire support role with excellent results even though they were not well suited for this job. As German resistance crumbled under the onslaught of such attacks the Allies drove deeper into the Third Reich. In late April Hitler committed suicide, ending the war in Europe.

In the Pacific, there was far less employment of tank destroyers than in Europe. They had first seen action in the Philippines as self-propelled artillery, but this was the only use by the Army of the M3 75mm GMC. However, the M3 was used extensively by the Marines in their Special Weapons Companies which were attached to each Marine division. Called Self-Propelled Mounts (SPMs) they provided direct fire support, although on a few occasions they helped repel Japanese tank attacks. Due to the close-in nature of jungle fighting and the ever present danger of snipers, these vehicles were often equipped with a large number of machine guns for protection as well as being covered by a large infantry component. The Marines used the M3 75mm GMC right up to the end of the war on Okinawa. The Marines had also used a small number of the M6 37mm GMCs early in the war but these were quickly phased out of service.

The Army deployed only seven tank destroyer battalions to the Pacific. Their first use came on the island of Kwajalein where M10s were used to support the 7th Infantry Division in place of tanks during February of 1944. Even more than in Europe, tank destroyers in the Pacific were used to provide direct fire support to infantry units but, again their open turret tops were not well liked due to the propensity of the Japanese for close-in combat. While tanks were much preferred, the tank destroyer units which were deployed saw extensive combat, particularly in the Philippines where three units saw fierce fighting. It was in the Philippines that the M18 was employed for the first time in the Pacific war. Toward the end of the war plans were made to deploy M36s to the Pacific for the invasion of Japan, but the Japanese surrender in September canceled these plans.

Under American Lend-Lease, M3 GMCs and M10s were supplied to the British while the Free French received the M3, M6, and M10 for their reconstituted armored formations. They were used mainly in the fire support role, although during the battle for France, the French M10s and British rearmed 17 pounder Achilles were used in their intended roles. A fairly large number of M3 Halftracks had been fitted early in the war with the 57mm cannon to meet a British requirement for a halftrack mounted tank destroyer, but these never saw service with the British Army. Designated the T48 57mm GMC, 650 were sent to Russia where they formed special independent tank destroyer battalions. Some were assigned to the Polish Army during the final months of the war

One of the most interesting uses of the M10 was by the Germans during the "Battle of the Bulge" in December 1944. The Germans modified ten Panther tanks to look like M10s using sheet metal and removing the commanders cupola. These were assigned to Otto Skorzeny's Panzer Brigade 150 which was to infiltrate the American lines and cause havoc in the rear areas. Although bearing a superficial resemblance to the M10 at a distance these Panther "M10s" were quickly knocked out in fierce fighting around Malmedy and failed completely in their mission of deception.

By the fall of 1944, tank destroyers were often being used as supplemental artillery in support of ground units due to shortages of artillery shells, especially in the heavy artillery class-

In late 1941 fifty T12's (pre-production M3s) were sent to the Philippines as a self-propelled artillery unit in support of the Provisional Tank Group which had been rushed to reinforce the islands. However, this unit was used mainly in the fire support role rather than as tank destroyers and gave valuable service throughout the campaign. Field reports indicated a need for more gun crew protection which led to a new gun shield being designed. (Green)

es of 155mm and above. Congressional criticism of large stockpile in North Africa led to production cutbacks in the fall of 1943. Production was restored in the spring of 1944, but the heavy shells were extremely complex and while production geared up, tank destroyers were one way to fill the gap as there was plenty of 3 inch and 76mm ammunition available.

An early T12 takes part in Army maneuvers in the fall of 1941. Much was learned during these training sessions with regards to tactics and employment of tank destroyers. The soldier holding the flag moves it to indicate when the gun was to be fired as live ammunition was not used during this training session. (USA/NA)

The first true taste of combat for the tank destroyers came during the battle for North Africa when Americans came up against battle hardened German armored units. After a number of disastrous encounters, revisions were made in tactics which helped the tank destroyers perform better in combat. Experience showed the M3 75mm GMC was not suited for this role and they were quickly replaced with the new fully tracked M10. The crew of this tank destroyer has camouflaged their vehicle with mud to help it blend in with the surrounding light colored soil. (PAM)

29

Another vehicle which was initially used in North Africa was the M6 37mm GMC. The light cannon proved to be worthless in the anti-tank role and the M6 was quickly pulled out of front-line service and the chassis converted back to a weapons carrier. Later some were provided to the new units of the Free French Army formed under the leadership of General De Gaulle. They soldiered on a little longer with US forces in the Pacific, but the M6 was a total failure as a tank destroyer. (USA/NA)

(Above) The M10 was first used in the later stages of the North African campaign. This M10 of the 899th Tank Destroyer Battalion moves up toward the front near Maknassy, Tunisia during the spring of 1943. The M10 proved a much better vehicle than the M3 75mm GMC with its hard-hitting 3 inch gun, greater mobility, and improved armor protection. It replaced M3s in the tank destroyer battalions as quickly as the vehicles were available. (USA/PAM)

(Below) By the time of the Sicily invasion, the M10 had become the standard tank destroyer in Army service. The commander of this M10 scans the area in front of him for signs of the enemy. The M10 is from the 601st TD Battalion and carries the common US star inside a circle which came into use in 1943. For the Sicily campaign the ring was sometimes painted yellow. (USA/NA)

(Above) In Sicily and Italy, the tank destroyer battalions were rarely used in their intended roles. Instead they were often parceled out to infantry and armored divisions where they provided fire support against German positions. These M10s from the 701st TD Battalion prepare to fire at German positions by the Arno River. An attempt has been made to break up the outline of the vehicles by adding tree branches and backing them into a small grove. (USA/NA)

(Left) In May of 1944, the Army sent two of the new T70 76mm GMC tank destroyers to the Anzio beachhead for field testing under combat conditions. Given a hasty camouflage pattern of black bands over their base coat of olive drab the new vehicles were well liked for their high speed and lower profile compared to the M10. The segmented ring around the star is a variation of the standard markings, usually due to the break in the stencil not being filled in by the paint depot work detail. (USA/NA)

(Below) When the Allies landed on D-Day, M10s were attached to most of the major formations to provide support. The dense hedgerow country was not conducive to large scale tank warfare and the opposing armies were locked in a deadly type of hide-and-seek. German troops examine a British Achilles which has received a number of hits, all of which penetrated the light side armor.

(Below) The crew of this M10 has added sandbags to the hull front in an attempt to provide additional protection against German guns. This is probably one of the earliest examples of this being done on the M10. The vehicle is taking part in the attack around St. Lo through thick hedgerow country. (USA/PAM)

(Above) In late July the Americans broke through the German lines which eventually led to a total collapse of the German front. This M10 fires on German positions near St. Lo during the initial stages of OPERATION COBRA. The deep wading trunk is still on the M10's rear. It allowed vehicles to come ashore without their engines being flooded. A large amount of extra gear is carried on the vehicle. (USA/NA)

(Below) Following the breakout from the Normandy bridgehead, the Allied armies fanned out across France in pursuit of the retreating German forces. This M10 moves through the town of Percy on August 1st. Close observation will show an added storage rack on the rear side of the hull for fuel cans. (USA/NA)

(Above) Members of the Winnipeg Rifles catch a ride on an M10 of the 3rd Anti-tank Regiment as the Canadians advance toward Gouy beyond the Seine River. The use of extra tracks for additional armor protection was common with British and Canadian armored units. (Canadian Archives)

(Below) An M10 attached to the 3rd Division, 7th Army, moves past destroyed German equipment and dead horses in the town of Montelimar, France at the end of August. The vehicle has been fitted with extra racks welded to the front to carry extra jerry cans of water as denoted by the 'W' painted on the can. (USA/NA)

The crew of "BATAAN" load ammunition into their vehicle during a lull in the fighting around Brest during mid-August 1944. Due to limited interior storage of the M18 the crew has secured much of their personal gear to the outside of the turret. The barrel has its underside painted white for countershading, much like the British did on the barrels of their Fireflies. The yellow circle on the side is the bridge weight marker. The name "POWDER RIVER" also appears on the gun barrel just forward of the canvas dust cover. (USA/NA)

(Above) Two M10s by-pass a destroyed bridge in central France late in the summer of 1944. Both are fitted with Culin hedgerow cutters which were developed to cut holes in the thick hedgerows of the Normandy countryside. Large amounts of extra fuel containers are carried on the rear deck to allow the vehicles to keep up a hot pursuit of the retreating Germans. (USA/NA)

(Below) Three late M10s from the 634th TD Battalion prepare to fire on a German observation post in Aachen, the first German city captured by the Allies, after fierce fighting in October of 1944. The first M10 is fitted with T48 rubber block track while the two in back appear to have T51 tracks which did not give as good traction as the T48 track. Each of the crews have added supplemental sandbag armor for protection against German handheld anti-tank weapons.

(Above) One of the unfortunate aspects of both the M10 and M18's design were their open topped turrets which exposed the crew to enemy fire, particularly in built-up areas. This M10 was knocked out while taking part in an attack on a French town. Under such conditions sniper fire, mortars, grenades, and hand-held anti-tank weapons were deadly against tank destroyers unless properly supported by infantry. (Green)

(Above) Two M10s fire on enemy positions in mid-September as the Allies pushed across France after the Wehrmacht collapse in August. The majority of the German armor was destroyed in the killing ground of the Falaise Pocket and few enemy tanks were encountered in the push toward Germany. (USA/NA)

(Below) The French Army received a large number of M10s for their reconstituted armored units. These M10s are from the *11e Regiment de Chasseurs d' Afrique* (11e RCA) which was attached to the French 5th Armored Division. The white diamond on the side of the hull is inside a box which has four alternating segments of blue and red around it, and outlined in white. (USA/NA)

(Above) In response to the request for heavier weapons to counter the heavy German armor encountered in Normandy, M36s armed with a 90mm gun began arriving in France during September. The crews of these M36s are undergoing training and familiarization with the new vehicles in mid- October. The 90mm gun of the M36 was the best American weapon at the time for dealing with Panthers and Tigers. (USA/NA)

37

(Above) This camouflaged M18 takes part in a fire support mission against German tanks during the fall of 1944. Shortages of heavy artillery ammunition at this stage of the war, required the use of TDs in the artillery support role since there was no shortage of 3 inch and 76mm ammunition. (USA/NA)

(Below) This late model M10 from the 804th TD Battalion provided artillery support fire for Fifth Army units during an attack on Sabiana, Italy in the fall of 1944. The large number of empty packing tubes and shell casings indicates just how intense the artillery barrage was. Tank destroyers were used extensively in the fire support role in Italy due to the lack of substantial numbers of German tanks because of the mountainous terrain which did not favor the large scale use of armor. (USA/NA)

(Above) This M36 has been sited in an elevated position in order to provide long range support fire. The crew has fitted wire mesh around the hull. It is believed that this M36 is from the 656th TD Battalion which was attached to the 9th Armored Division. (USA/NA)

(Above) By the end of October the M36 had started to reach the front. This M36 from the 607th TD Battalion covers a street in the French town of Metz in late November 1944, General George Patton's Third Army captured the town after a two month campaign which started in September. (US Army Signal Corps)

(Below) An M10 from the 645th TD Battalion moves through a roadblock consisting of a double row of logs filled with debris in the French town of Lembach just prior to the start of the Ardennes offensive. The town was a key road junction and had just been captured by elements of the Seventh Army. (USA/NA)

(Above) The front of this M10 has been covered with sandbags and wire mesh to hold them in place. The top of the turret has also been fitted with a partial armored roof supported by metal rods which still allows for adequate visibility while under cover. (USA/NA)

(Below) This M36 has been camouflaged with whitewash to blend in better with the snowy conditions which existed in the latter stages of the Battle of the Bulge. It is attached to General Patton's Third Army and is taking part in operations in Luxembourg during the first week of January 1945. (USA/NA)

(Above) This group of three M18s await orders to move up toward the front from the town of Perl. They are from the 705th TD Battalion which was attached to the 10th Armored Division. By this stage of the war, German armor was rarely encountered. (USA/NA)

(Below) This destroyed M18 of the 704th TD Battalion was knocked out south of Bastogne. Attached to the 4th Armored Division, the unit was taking part in the relief attempt when it was hit by artillery fire, which proved deadly against the thin skin and open top of the M18. (Green)

(Above) In mid-December 1944 Hitler launched the Ardennes Offensive. The attack caught the Americans off-guard and enjoyed considerable success. Reinforcements were rushed to the front to help the beleaguered U.S. troops. These M36s move up to support the 82nd Airborne Division four days after the start of the offensive. The heavy gun was especially needed by the airborne forces which had no weapons which could tackle German armor with any hope of success. (USA/NA)

(Below) The icy roads could be almost as dangerous as the Germans if proper care was not taken. This M36 from the 702nd TD Battalion, 2nd Armored Division slid off the road while being towed to an ordnance shop for repairs, killing a number of GIs in the resulting collision. It appears that the star on the turret has been covered over with mud to eliminate it as an aiming point for German gunners. (USA/NA)

(Above) An M10 from the 773rd TD Battalion moves up in support of elements of the 90th Infantry Division during operations in Berle, Luxembourg. The operation was aimed at dislodging the southern flank of the German salient in mid-January. (USA/NA)

A heavily sandbagged M18 negotiates a curve in the road near Fisenne, Belgium in late January. White sheets and cloth as well as snow were used in lieu of whitewash which was often not available in the field. In one case the people of a Belgian town donated their white household linen to help the Americans camouflage their vehicles. (USA/NA)

After the Ardennes Offensive the threat from German tanks was greatly diminished due to the heavy losses they had suffered in the battle. However, the threat from hand-held weapons such as the Panzerfaust became even greater as the Allies advanced through towns. The crew of this M10 has added sandbags and logs in an effort to improve their protection against such weapons. The vehicle is still fitted with a Culin hedgerow cutter used during the Normandy breakout in July. (USA/NA)

The crew of this 773rd TD Battalion M10 has painted their vehicle with white vertical stripes, helping it to blend into the tree line, the Olive Drab giving the impression of tree trunks and foliage. Two .30 caliber machine guns are fitted to the turret. In addition, a possible screen for overhead cover is on the rear of the turret. The tube extending out from the hull from the jerry can was for a pole used to drape camouflage netting over the vehicle. (USA/NA)

A rare sight in the combat zone was this M36B1, the version mating the M36 turret with a Sherman tank hull. This was the only U.S. tank destroyer which carried a hull machine gun. From the 654th TD Battalion the crew of this vehicle has been credited with knocking out two Tigers and two Panzer IVs and carries four victory markings on the mantlet. The odd shaped attachments on the treads are duck-billed end connectors which could be added to lessen ground pressure and give better mobility in muddy conditions. (USA/NA)

A well-worn M10 of the 636th TD Battalion passes through the French town of Rohrwiller in early February. The battalion was attached to the 143rd Regiment of the 36th Infantry Division which was advancing toward the German border. (USA/NA)

A camouflaged M10 fires on enemy positions in the Mt. Belvedere area of Italy in late February of 1945. The drive sprocket is a variation of the original type used on the M3/M4 series of medium tanks, while the road wheels are the early open spoke variety. Duckbill end connectors are fitted to the T48 track to improve the flotation over muddy terrain. (USA/NA)

An M10 fires on German positions across the Sauer River near the Luxembourg town of Echtermach in the first week of February 1945. The vehicle carries a large amount of extra gear and twin storage racks which have been added to the rear deck. The remnants of whitewash camouflage can be seen on the rear and sides of the turret. (USA/NA)

The crew of this M10 has added extra sandbags to the front of their vehicle's hull for additional protection from German tank fire and infantry anti-tank weapons. The spare road-wheels also aided in this task. These wheels are solid with embossed spokes. This M10 is also fitted with the Culin hedgerow cutter which was welded to the front of the transmission cover. (Green)

43

(Above) Framed by the burning town of Irsch, Germany, an M18 watches for any sign of enemy activity. The large markings on the turret side were felt to be necessary for identification purposes as the M18's suspension was similar to some German types. (USA/NA)

(Below) An M18 carrying a load of GIs from the 255th Battalion, 63rd Infantry Division, moves down the autobahn near Scheppach in southern Germany. The M18 was the fastest American AFV of World War Two and from the looks of the tracks this Hellcat must have been traveling close to its top speed. The 76mm gun has been fitted with a muzzle brake which was done late in the M18 production run. (USA/NA)

(Above) An M36 from the 5th Armored Division, Ninth Army fires on German positions in the town of Tangermunde, Germany in April of 1945. The vehicle has been fitted with an armored cover around the open-topped turret for additional protection. Close infantry support was a vital necessity in the close confines of towns during the advance through Germany in the face of sometimes fanatical resistance. (USA/NA)

44

A soldier of the 301st Infantry Regt, 94th Infantry Division runs for cover past a but-toned up M36 in the German town of Schillingen in March of 1945. The M36 is equipped with T45 steel chevron track. The crew has moved the .50 caliber machine gun to the front of the turret for a better field of fire forward. (USA/NA)

(Above) The first Pacific use of the M10 took place during the invasion of Kwajalein in February of 1944 by the 767th TD Battalion. They were used as "bunker busters" since their 3 inch gun packed a more powerful punch than the 75mm cannon of the M4 medium tank. The open top of the M10 was even more of a hazard in the Pacific than in Europe due to the close assault tactics used by Japanese infantry. The lower rear of this vehicle shows the remains of the sealing compound used on the wading gear fitting for coming ashore. (USA/NA)

(Below) The first group of the new M18s began arriving in the summer of 1944. The crews of these Hellcats prepare their new vehicles for deployment at Espiritu Santo in the New Hebrides. The M18s were assigned to the 637th TD Battalion. While these vehicles are fitted with fender guards some of the flimsy sheet metal already shows damage from their transportation to the Pacific. These were usually ripped off in action after only a short time and were rarely replaced. (USA/NA)

(Above) The crews of these two M10s await orders to move out against new targets on Kwajalein. Close infantry support was a vital requirement to protect the vulnerable vehicles against close-in assault by Japanese infantry. (USA/NA)

(Above) Infantrymen from the 37th Infantry Division sprint past a Hellcat of the 637th TD battalion. The machine gunner is covering the rear against possible Japanese attackers who may have played possum and let the vehicle pass in order to surprise it from the rear. The object of the advance is the Luzon town of Baguio. Extra gear was often tied down to the front of M18s due to limited internal stowage space. (USA/NA)

The first large scale employment of tank destroyer units was during the Philippine campaign where three battalions, the 632nd, 637th, and 640th were deployed. This 632d Battalion M10 moves along a village street on northwest Leyte in support of elements of the 77th Infantry Division. The rear angle of the turret indicates it is a late model M10. (USA/NA)

(Above) The last use of tank destroyers in the Pacific was during the attack on Okinawa. The commander directs fire from this M18 against Japanese positions on the Shuri Line in May of 1945. The crew has fitted a .30 caliber machine gun to the right side of the vehicle for additional protection. The lighter and easier to handle .30 caliber weapon was often more effective against close assaults by Japanese infantry (USA/NA)

While the gun commander scans the far shore for signs of more targets at Ormac Bay, Leyte, the crew of this late production M10 carries out general maintenance on their vehicle. Japanese barges, which the M10 hit earlier, blaze in the background. The vehicle retains it's deep wading trunk on the hull rear. (USA/NA)

47

(Above) When the Korean War broke out in June of 1950, there were no tank destroyers in the Army inventory. However, when the fighting finally stabilized M36s in storage were sent to help rebuild the South Korean forces. This M36 has been modernized by the installation of the M3A1 90mm gun with a single baffle muzzle brake and bore evacuator. It belongs to the 53rd ROK Tank Company. A crude shield of sandbags and logs has been added to the turret for additional protection. (USA/NA)

(Below) A Canadian Achilles from the 25th Canadian Infantry Brigade is unloaded in South Korea in March of 1952. In order to standardize on common equipment and due to the opened topped nature of the turret, the Achilles were replaced by M4A3E8 Sherman tanks which were better suited to the fighting in Korea. (Public Archives Canada via Storey)

(Above) The crews of these M36B2s replenish their ammunition stores after a prolonged fire support mission against communist positions on White Horse Mountain north of Chorwon in October of 1952. The vehicles are camouflaged in a two-tone scheme of olive drab and light brown. The tracks on the left M36 are fitted with duckbilled end connectors to increase flotation in the mud. (USA/NA)

French M36B2s were fitted with folding overhead armor to protect the open turret. Even so, close infantry support was a must. Many crews fitted machine guns for better close-in defense against Viet Minh infantry attacks. The RBCEO insignia, a white knight's helmet and cannons over a yellow anchor can be seen on the turret side. (ECPA via Balin)

Concern over possible Chinese intervention with heavy tanks such as the JS-II led to the deployment of the *Regiment Blinde Colonial d' Extreme Orient* (RBCEO) equipped with M36B2s to Indochina. The Chinese threat never materialized so the M36s were used to provide fire support for French Union Forces. (ECPA via Balin)

The last use of American tank destroyers took place in the bitter fighting which wracked Yugoslavia. Croatian forces used M36B2s while the Serbian troops employed M18s. These had been supplied in the early 1950's under the Military Assistance Program (MAP) when the U.S. tried to undercut Soviet influence in the country. This captured M36B2 is being taken away by UN peacekeeping forces. (Spencer)

This Serbian M18 was one of several which ended up under United Nations control following the Dayton cease-fire accord. The vehicle is overall medium green with a camouflage pattern of red-brown and black sprayed randomly over it. The crest to the left is blue with yellow detail and outline while the larger outline around it is in blue. The purpose of the brackets on the lower front hull is unknown. (Cole)

49